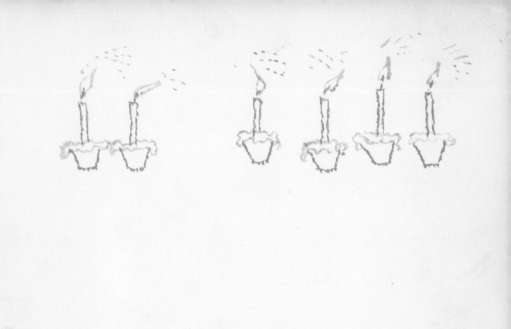

THE BIRTHDAY PARTY

by Ruth Krauss

pictures by Maurice Sendak

Harper and Brothers – Publishers – New York

THE BIRTHDAY PARTY—TEXT COPYRIGHT ©1957 BY RUTH KRAUSS—PICTURES COPYRIGHT ©1957 BY MAURICE SENDAK
PRINTED IN THE UNITED STATES OF AMERICA
ALL RIGHTS IN THIS BOOK ARE RESERVED—LIBRARY OF CONGRESS CATALOG CARD NUMBER: 57-5353

E

11-14-57

A boy, David, had been EVERYWHERE.

He had been to the beach.

He had been to the woods.

He had been to the corner alone.

But he had never been to a birthday party.
And he wanted to have been to a birthday party.
One day David came in the house.

Looked upstairs.
Nobody there.

Looked in the kitchen.
Nobody there.

Looked in the dining room.

EVERYBODY there —
came up popping out of all the chairs singing
HAPPY—

—BIRTHDAY to you HAPPY BIRTHDAY to you
HAPPY BIRTHDAY dear —

— DAVID—

and when he heard them and his name
he knew at last he was at a birthday party
and that birthday party was —

HIS OWN.